A BOOK OF SPECIAL DAYS

A LION BOOK
Tring · Batavia · Sydney

Special events this month

There are many special memories in our lives that deserve to be recorded. There are birthdays, wedding days, anniversaries, events that we want to remember and treasure.

This book is designed to meet this simple need, and at the same time celebrate anniversaries of people of faith down the ages. In this way it becomes not only a keepsake of special memories, but a source of inspiration for the passing years. Here are recorded the lives of men and women – some ordinary people whose lives have been touched by God, others out-of-the-ordinary, explorers, pioneers, scientists, great men and women of faith and vision. It is hoped that their example will stimulate and inspire those who follow in their footsteps.

JANUARY

Friars Balsam

1

Died 379, Basil the Great, the Greek bishop who laid down the principles still practised by monks in the Orthodox tradition.

2

3

JANUARY

4

Born 1809, Louis Braille, the blind Frenchman who devised the touch system of reading and writing for the blind.

5

6

Died 1884, Gregor Mendel, the monk from Heinzendorf (now in Czechoslovakia) whose work on different strains of peas laid the basis for modern genetics.

7

Born 1873, Charles Peguy, French poet, publisher and campaigner for the rights of the poor.

8

Died 1941, Robert Baden-Powell, founder of the Boy Scout movement.

JANUARY

9

Born 1724, Isaac Backus, American historian and itinerant Baptist preacher.

_____

_____

_____

10

_____

_____

_____

_____

11

Born 1903, Alan Paton, South African writer and educator, whose works show the inseparability of Christian faith and social concern.

_____

_____

_____

'Oh Love that lightenest all my ways
Within, without, below, above,
Flow through the minutes of my days,
The sum of all my life be love.'

Amy Carmichael
1867–1951

JANUARY

12

13

Died 1915, Mary Slessor, the Scots missionary who worked among the people of the African forest.

14

Born 1847, Wilson Carlile, founder of the Church Army, whose work with the poor of the inner cities started in the East End of London.

15

Born 1929, Martin Luther King Jr, American negro clergyman and civil rights leader who spearheaded non-violent resistance to racial segregation.

16

JANUARY

17

18

Died 1951, Amy Carmichael, the Irish missionary-poet who worked in India for over fifty years, and founded the Dohnavur Mission to give hope to hundreds of boys and girls.

19

Martyred 1160, Henry of Uppsala, English bishop and patron saint of Finland.

'*I have a dream that my four little children one day will live in a nation where they will not be judged by the color of their skin but by the content of their character.*

I have a dream today.

I have a dream that one day the state of Alabama, whose governor's lips are presently dripping with the words of interposition and nullification, will be transformed into a situation where little black boys and black girls will be able to join hands with little white boys and white girls and walk together as sisters and brothers.

I have a dream today.'

Martin Luther King Jr
1928–68

JANUARY

20

*Died 1569, Miles Coverdale, Augustinian monk, bishop and translator
of the first printed English Bible.*

21

22

23

*Died 1875, Charles Kingsley, English novelist, social reformer and chaplain
to Queen Victoria.*

24

*Born 1818, John Mason Neale, the clergyman who founded
the nursing sisterhood of St Margaret, and wrote many hymns
including 'Good Christian men rejoice!'*

JANUARY

25

26

The feast day of Polycarp, a bishop in western Asia Minor, martyred on 23 February 155 because he would not renounce his faith.

27

Born 1832, Charles Dodgson, English clergyman, mathematician and, as Lewis Carroll, famous author of children's books.

Then Polycarp was led away and there was a great uproar. He was led before the Proconsul who asked him his name. The Proconsul tried to persuade him to change his mind saying "Have respect for your age. Swear by the genius of Caesar and say 'Away with the atheists.' " Then Polycarp looked sternly at the noisy mob in the stadium and waving his hand at them said "Away with the atheists". But the Proconsul urged him and said "Swear, and I will release you; curse the Christ." Polycarp said "Eighty-six years have I served him and he has done me no wrong. How then can I blaspheme my king who saved me?"

About a century after the death of Jesus, Polycarp died at the hands of those who would make him swear allegiance to Caesar instead of Christ.

JANUARY

28

Born 1856, Reuben Archer Torrey, American minister, bestselling author, powerful evangelist and outstanding teacher.

29

30

31

Died 1561, Menno Simons, Dutch radical Reformation leader who gave his name to the Mennonite churches, noted for their rejection of war and violence.

Mountain range
by Martin Thonig

Special events this month

FEBRUARY

Nasturtiums

1

2

In 1864, Fanny Crosby, blind since childhood, began her hymn-writing career when she met William Bradberry, famous hymnwriter and publisher.

3

Welsh politician and Methodist local preacher George Thomas was elected Speaker of the British House of Commons in 1976.

FEBRUARY

4

*Born 1906, Dietrich Bonhoeffer, the German Lutheran pastor executed
for his involvement in a plot to assassinate Hitler.*

5

*Born 1837, Dwight Moody, American evangelist, who, with Ira Sankey,
organized revival campaigns in England and the USA.*

6

7

8

FEBRUARY

9

Died 444, Cyril of Alexandria, who defended the doctrine of the divinity and humanity of Christ.

10

Born 1824, Samuel Plimsoll, 'the sailors' friend', who succeeded in improving conditions for sailors of the merchant fleet.

11

The feast day of Caedmon, a seventh-century cowherd with a gift for poetry which he used in praise of God.

> '*Now ought we to praise*
> *the founder of the heavenly kingdom,*
> *the power of the Creator, and His wise design,*
> *the deeds of the Father of glory;*
> *how He, eternal God,*
> *was the author of all things wonderful,*
> *who first created for the sons of men*
> *the heaven for a roof, and afterwards the earth –*
> *He, the almighty guardian of mankind.*'

Caedmon
Seventh-century poet and father of English verse

FEBRUARY

12

Born 1809, Abraham Lincoln, who overcame humble origins to become the sixteenth president of the USA, and fought for the abolition of slavery.

13

14

15

Born 1564, Galileo Galilei, Italian astronomer, mathematician and physicist, who paved the way for freedom of expression for science.

16

Born 1766, Thomas Malthus, English economist who advanced his population theory in 'An Essay on the Principle of Population'.

FEBRUARY

17

*In 1977, Janani Luwum, Anglican Archbishop of Uganda, was murdered
for his opposition to the regime of Idi Amin.*

18

19

*Died 1845, Thomas Buxton, British politician and explorer,
a leader in the campaign against slavery.*

Janani Luwum
1922–77

In February 1977 the congregation of Namirembe Cathedral in
Kampala met around an empty grave. The body of the Anglican
Archbishop of Uganda, Janani Luwum, was not released by the
authorities for the funeral.

Janani, a member of the Acholi tribe of Uganda, had been
converted after the East African revival of the late 1930s.

Later, as Archbishop, he was known for his warmth and courage.
Under the regime of Idi Amin he had preached the Christian gospel,
praying for the president and the security forces. But when he wrote a
letter to the president about the hundreds of ordinary men and women
who had been taken to prison and were never seen again, he knew he
was signing his death warrant.

As the congregation looked on the gaping hole in the earth, they
realized together the heart of the gospel message: the empty tomb, the
resurrection of the body and the reality of the living Christ.

FEBRUARY

20

21

Died 1945 in a Japanese prisoner-of-war camp, Eric Liddell,
Scots missionary and Olympic Gold Medallist.

22

Died 1845, Sydney Smith, poor English clergyman and wit, who improved
conditions of his even poorer parishioners.

23

Died 1468, Johann Gutenberg, pioneer German printer who made possible
the distribution of the Bible for ordinary people.

24

Born 1766, Samuel Wesley, English composer, organist and author, aged 11,
of 'Eight Lessons for the Harpsichord'.

FEBRUARY

25

*Died 1723, Christopher Wren, British architect
and designer of St Paul's Cathedral, London.*

26

27

*Born 1807, Henry Wadsworth Longfellow, American poet who wrote the epic
'The Song of Hiawatha'.*

Eric Liddell
1902–45

Scots athlete Eric Liddell, hero of the film *Chariots of Fire*, was the son
of missionary parents who came to fame when he won a gold medal on
11 July 1924 in the Paris Olympic Games.

Liddell had been chosen to represent Great Britain in the 100
metres, but when he discovered that the heats were to be run on a
Sunday he refused to enter. It became apparent that he would not
compromise his principles for anyone, and it was only at the last
moment that he was entered for the 400 metres, an event for which he
was untrained. He amazed everyone by winning the gold medal.

Liddell later went as a missionary to China, where he died in 1945 in
a prisoner-of-war camp.

FEBRUARY

28

Born 1911, Denis Burkitt, Irish doctor and proponent of the high fibre diet,
who first found a cure for a form of childhood cancer.

29

Windmills
by Shogi Kotoh

Special events this month

MARCH

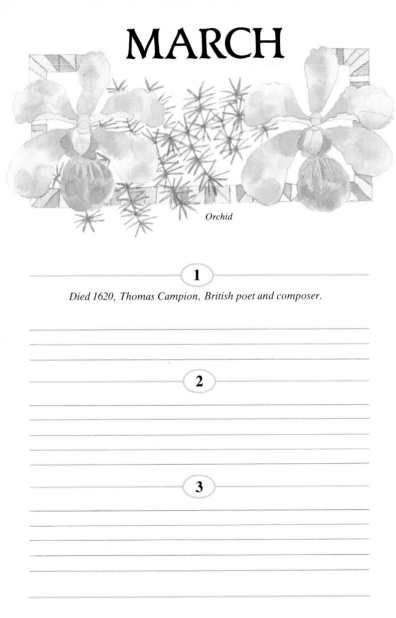

Orchid

1

Died 1620, Thomas Campion, British poet and composer.

2

3

MARCH

4

5

6

Born 1475, Michelangelo Buonarroti, Italian sculptor, painter,
architect and poet, whose amazing output
includes the ceiling of the Sistine Chapel in Rome.

7

Died 1274, Thomas Aquinas, Italian theologian whose writings formed
the thinking of many generations of theologians.

8

Died 1717, Abraham Darby, the Quaker ironmaster who was the first person
to use coke to smelt iron.

MARCH

9

Died 395, Gregory of Nyssa, bishop and theologian, a greatly respected figure in the Eastern church, noted for the depth of his writings.

10

11

Born 1926, Ralph Abernathy, American clergyman and civil rights leader.

'Give me, O Lord, a steadfast heart,
which no unworthy affection may drag downwards;
give me an unconquered heart,
which no tribulation can wear out;
give me an upright heart,
which no unworthy purpose may tempt aside.
Bestow on me also, O Lord my God,
understanding to know you,
diligence to seek you,
wisdom to find you,
and a faithfulness that may finally embrace you,
through Jesus Christ our Lord, Amen.'

Thomas Aquinas
1225–74

MARCH

12

In 1843, Robert Murray McCheyne, Scots pastor and writer, preached his last sermon.

13

14

Died 968, Matilda, wife of the German King Henry I, much loved for her concern for the poor and needy.

15

Died 1660, Louise de Marillac, founder of the religious order of the Daughters of Charity, known for their work among the sick.

16

Died 1021, Herbert of Cologne, German bishop and man of peace.

MARCH

17

18

19

Born 1813, David Livingstone, Scots doctor, explorer and missionary.

David Livingstone
1813–73

David Livingstone was in his twenties when he offered himself for missionary service and went to South Africa as a doctor. Much of the land was still uncharted and, eager to take the Christian gospel into new territory, he made three major expeditions, discovering the Victoria Falls on one of them.

Apart from laying the foundation for later missionary work, Livingstone sought to expose the slave trade in Africa, about which he was deeply concerned.

As an explorer, he probably did more for African geography than any other, and eventually died in the attempt to discover the source of the Nile.

MARCH

20

*The feast day of Cuthbert, pioneer of the Celtic church in Britain
who lived on the island of Lindisfarne, and died in 687 after devoting his life
to the needs of others.*

21

22

*Died 1758, Jonathan Edwards, American Puritan preacher and writer,
an outstanding intellect and leader of the Great Awakening revival.*

23

24

*In 1980, Oscar Romero, Archbishop of San Salvador and campaigner
for the rights of the poor, was murdered in his own cathedral.*

25

Died 1877, Caroline Chisholm, Australian philanthropist noted particularly for her work among immigrant girls.

26

27

Oscar Romero
1917–80

Oscar Romero was a man of peace. As Archbishop of San Salvador he was outspoken against injustice, poverty, violence and oppression, whether by government forces or terrorist groups. Through his faith in God he worked towards a just solution to the problems of El Salvador.

On 24 March 1980 he was shot dead by a right-wing death squad of four masked gunmen while celebrating mass in his own cathedral.

Two weeks before, he had spoken these words: 'Martyrdom is a grace from God which I do not believe I deserve. But if God accepts the sacrifice of my life, then may my blood be the seed of liberty, and a sign that hope will soon become a reality.'

MARCH

28

*Born 1592, John Comenius, educational reformer and a leader
of the Moravian and Bohemian Brethren.*

29

30

*Died 1945, Mother Maria (Elizabeth Pilenko),
a nun from a wealthy Russian family, who went voluntarily to the gas chambers
at Ravensbruck to comfort a young Jewish girl.*

31

Died 1631, John Donne, poet and Dean of St Paul's Cathedral, London.

Waterfall
by Gerols Kalt

Special events this month

APRIL

Sweet Pea

1

2

Born 1827, Holman Hunt, artist of the Pre-Raphaelite Brotherhood and painter of 'The Light of the World'.

3

Born 1593, George Herbert, poet and hymnwriter, who wrote the poem 'Love' and whose hymns include 'Let all the world in every corner sing'.

APRIL

4

5

*Died 1811, Robert Raikes, printer who, in 1780, pioneered
the Sunday school movement.*

6

*Died 1528, Albrecht Dürer, German printer, engraver, woodcut artist and
writer, famous for his biblical illustrations and praying 'Hands'.*

7

*Born 1506, St Francis Xavier, Spanish missionary and one of the founders
of the Jesuit order.*

8

APRIL

9

10

*Born 1829, William Booth, English founder and first general
of the Salvation Army.*

11

'*No man is an island, entire of itself,
every man is a piece of the continent,
a part of the main.*'

John Donne
1573–1631

APRIL

12

13

14

The feast day of Justin, born in Samaria, who wrote vigorously in defence of the Christian gospel until his martyrdom in 165.

15

Died 1889, Father Joseph Damien, the Belgian priest who gave up his life working in the leper colony at Molokai, Hawaii.

16

Died 1825, Henry Fuseli, Anglo-Swiss author and painter, famous for his painting of the three witches from 'Macbeth'.

APRIL

17

18

Died 1909, William Smith, writer, poet and Archbishop of Sydney.

19

William Booth
1829–1912

William Booth's work led to his unpopularity among churchmen and brewers alike. His preaching career began among slum-dwellers and although he was a minister in the Methodist Church for a while, his concern for the needy took him back to the slums.

In 1865, he and his wife Catherine began their own Christian mission in a tent in Whitechapel, London – a venture that was to grow into the Salvation Army. Originally a revivalist organization, it never lost sight of the plight of the poor, and is still concerned with the needs of people without food or shelter today.

APRIL

20

Died 1759, George Frederick Handel, German-born composer famous for his oratorio 'The Messiah'.

21

Died 1109, Anselm, Archbishop of Canterbury, who in his book 'Proslogion' attempted to prove by logic the existence of God.

22

23

Born 1621, William Penn, English Quaker and founder of Pennsylvania.

24

APRIL

25

Died 1800, William Cowper, English poet and hymnwriter, who suffered from depression for most of his life, yet contributed many hymns to the Olney hymnbook.

26

27

'Oh! for a closer walk with God,
A calm and heavenly frame;
A light to shine upon the road
That leads me to the Lamb!

What peaceful hours I once enjoyed!
How sweet their memory still!
But they have left an aching void,
The world can never fill.'

William Cowper
1731–1800

APRIL

28

Born 1801, Anthony Ashley Cooper, seventh Earl of Shaftesbury, English evangelical churchman and social reformer who promoted measures to improve conditions in mines, factories and schools.

29

30

In 1789 George Washington was inaugurated as first president of the USA.

Bulb fields
by Shogi Kotoh

Special events this month

MAY

Creeping Jenny

1

2

Died 1519, Leonardo da Vinci, Italian painter, sculptor, architect and engineer, a leading figure of the Italian Renaissance.

3

Baptized 1850, Charles Haddon Spurgeon, leading Baptist orator, preacher and prolific author, who drew thousands to hear him speak.

MAY

4

5

*Born 1813, Søren Kierkegaard, Danish philosopher and theologian who
emphasized man's moral responsibility and freedom of choice.*

6

7

*Born 1812, Robert Browning, famous for his dramatic monologues
and the poem 'Pippa's Song' which ends
'God's in his heaven – all's right with the world!'*

8

*Born 1828, Jean Henri Dunant, Swiss founder of the Red Cross
and winner of the Nobel peace prize in 1901.*

MAY

9

Died 1706, Count Nikolaus Ludwig von Zinzendorf, German reformer, hymnwriter and leader of the Moravian Church, one of the influences on John Wesley and hence the Methodist movement.

10

Born 1886, Karl Barth, Swiss Protestant theologian and opponent of Nazism.

11

Died 1621, Johann Arndt, Lutheran theologian and mystic.

'O Lord, heavenly Father, in whom is the fulness of light and wisdom, enlighten our minds by your Holy Spirit, and give us grace to receive your Word with reverence and humility, without which no one can understand your truth.'

John Calvin
1509–64

MAY

12

Born 1820, Florence Nightingale, English nurse famous for her work during the Crimean War and founder of modern nursing.

13

The feast day of Julian of Norwich, remembered not only for her mystical experiences but the depth of her theology.

14

Died 1881, Mary Seacole, Jamaican-born nurse who developed a medicine to treat cholera.

15

In 1919, Eglantyne Jebb was fined for trying to help the starving children of the world, resulting in the founding of the Save the Children Fund.

16

Died 1945, George Campbell Morgan, one of the great preachers of the early twentieth century, who was once rejected as unsuitable for the ministry.

MAY

(17)

(18)

(19)

'God, of your goodness, give me yourself; for you are sufficient for me. I cannot properly ask anything less, to be worthy of you. If I were to ask less, I should always be in want. In you alone do I have all.'

Julian of Norwich
Fourteenth-century mystic

MAY

20

21

Born 1780, Elizabeth Fry, English Quaker, prison and hospital reformer.

22

23

Born 1749, Edward Jenner, the English physician who was the first to establish the principle of vaccination with his studies on smallpox.

24

Died 1543, Nicolas Copernicus, Polish astronomer who proposed that the sun was the centre of the solar system.

MAY

25

*Died 735, the Venerable Bede, monk, scholar and historian, who recorded
the life and faith of the Celtic church in Britain and translated
part of the Bible into the language of the English people.*

26

*Died 605, Augustine, first Archbishop of Canterbury and founder of the church
in southern England.*

27

*Died 1564, John Calvin, French theologian and leader of the Reformation
in France and Switzerland.*

'*When we compare the present life of man with that time
of which we have no knowledge, it seems to be like the
swift flight of a lone sparrow through the banqueting-hall
. . . This sparrow flies swiftly in through one door of the
hall, and out through another . . . Similarly, man
appears on earth for a little while, but we know nothing
of what went on before this life, and what follows.*'

Bede
Eighth-century historian

MAY

28

Died 1849, Anne Brontë, English novelist, poet and hymnwriter.

29

30

31

Springtime in the Alps
by Freidmar Damm

Special events this month

JUNE

Common Vetch

---

(1)

Born 1793, Henry Francis Lyte, the hymnwriter who, shortly before his death, wrote the famous hymn 'Abide With Me'.

---

(2)

---

(3)

Died 1905, James Hudson Taylor, pioneer missionary who adopted the lifestyle of the Chinese people to bring the Christian gospel to China.

JUNE

4

5

6

Born 1911, Alan Walker, Australian founder of Lifeline International and active campaigner for the disadvantaged.

7

8

Died 1889, Gerard Manley Hopkins, the poet-priest whose innovative use of language gave poems such as 'God's Grandeur' and 'Pied Beauty' such power.

JUNE

9

The feast day of Columba of Iona, the abbot and missionary who preached and taught among the Picts, and died in 597.

10

Born 1801, Joseph Rowntree, English Quaker businessman who worked to improve the education system and the life of the mentally handicapped.

11

'Glory be to God for dappled things –
For skies of couple-colour as a brindled cow;
For rose-moles all in stipple upon trout that swim;
Fresh firecoal chestnut-falls; finches' wings;
Landscapes plotted and pierced – fold, fallow, and plough;
And all trades, their gear and tackle and trim.

All things counter, original, spare, strange;
Whatever is fickle, freckled (who knows how?)
With swift, slow; sweet, sour; adazzle, dim;
He fathers-forth whose beauty is past change:
Praise him.'

Gerard Manley Hopkins
1844–89

JUNE

―――――――――― **12** ――――――――――

―――――――――― **13** ――――――――――

*Born 1893, Dorothy L. Sayers, English detective-story writer
and author of the play about Jesus' life, 'The Man Born to be King'.*

―――――――――― **14** ――――――――――

*Born 1811, Harriet Beecher Stowe, anti-slavery campaigner who risked
imprisonment by helping runaway slaves, and author of 'Uncle Tom's Cabin'.*

―――――――――― **15** ――――――――――

―――――――――― **16** ――――――――――

JUNE

17

Born 1703, John Wesley, preacher of some 40,000 sermons, evangelist, writer and one of the founders of the Methodist movement.

18

19

Born 1914, Metropolitan Anthony, doctor, French Resistance fighter and head of the Russian Orthodox Patriarchal Church in Britain.

'*I now stood and looked back on the past year; a year of uncommon trials and uncommon blessings. Abundance have been convinced of sin; very many have found peace with God; and in London only, I believe, full two hundred have been brought into glorious liberty. And yet I have had more care and trouble in six months than in several years preceding. What the end will be, I know not; but it is enough that God knoweth.*'

John Wesley
1703–91

JUNE

20

21

22

*Died 1714, Matthew Henry, English nonconformist minister and author
of a famous commentary on the whole Bible.*

23

24

*Born 1764, Samuel Marsden, Australian philanthropist
and pioneer missionary to New Zealand's Maori population.*

25

26

In 1736, George Whitefield, one of the founders of the Methodist movement,
preached his first sermon.

27

George Whitefield
1714–70

Influenced by John and Charles Wesley while at Oxford University,
Whitefield was ordained in 1736 and went to work in Georgia in the
USA. On his return to England, he was not accepted in the parish
pulpits and was forced to preach in the open air, an example later
followed by John Wesley.

A persuasive speaker with a simple style, he became a great
evangelist. The famous English actor, David Garrick, once said, 'I
would give 100 guineas if I could say "Oh" like Mr Whitefield.' He
travelled extensively in England, Scotland and Wales, and made seven
visits to the USA, becoming a leading figure in the revival known as the
Great Awakening.

JUNE

28

Born 1865, David Young Cameron, Scots painter and etcher who appealed for a greater recognition of the arts by the church.

29

In 1864, Samuel Crowther, one-time Nigerian slave, became the first black Anglican bishop.

30

Died 1861, Elizabeth Barratt Browning, child prodigy and popular English poet, best known for her love poems 'Sonnets from the Portuguese'.

Pathway
by Sonia Halliday

Special events this month

JULY

Poppy

1

2

*Born 1489, Thomas Cranmer, English scholar,
first Protestant Archbishop of Canterbury,
and compiler of 'The Book of Common Prayer'.*

3

JULY

4

Born 1845, Thomas Barnardo, Irish founder of homes for destitute children.

5

6

Died 1415, Jan Hus, the Czech preacher who wrote in Latin and Czech to reach both academic and layman, and whose recovery of the Christian gospel and reform of the church made him one of the forerunners of the Reformation.

7

8

JULY

9

*Died 1228, Stephen Langton, who divided the books of the Bible
into the chapters which are still used today.*

10

*Born 1888, Dr Toyohiko Kagawa, Japanese preacher, poet, social reformer
and pacifist, who helped the poor of the docklands in Shinkawa, Japan.*

11

Thomas Barnardo
1845–1905

After his conversion to Christianity in 1862, Dublin-born Barnardo
went to London to study medicine, intending to go as a medical
missionary to China. The course of his life was changed when he
encountered the conditions of the poor and destitute of England's
capital city. He befriended a young orphan boy, and was taken 'home'
to the warehouse roof in the East End where he slept. Shocked by
these conditions, Barnardo began a campaign on behalf of orphan
children, using photographs of children in poverty as part of his
publicity and becoming one of the first to set up children's homes.

JULY

12

Died 1536, Desiderius Erasmus, Dutch scholar and translator of the Bible, an influential moderate in the Protestant Reformation.

13

Born 1793, John Clare, English shepherd and peasant poet, who noted down ideas for his verses on the crown of his hat while he worked in the fields.

14

15

Born 1606, Rembrandt, Dutch artist famous for his painting 'The Night Watch'.

16

JULY

17

Born 1674, Isaac Watts, poet, linguist and preacher, who at twenty criticized the metrical psalms used in church worship and went on to write some 750 hymns of his own.

18

Born 1720, Gilbert White, clergyman and naturalist, author of 'The Natural History and Antiquities of Selborne'.

19

'When I survey the wondrous cross
    On which the Prince of glory died,
My richest gain I count but loss,
    And pour contempt on all my pride.

Were the whole realm of Nature mine,
    That were an offering far too small;
Love so amazing, so divine,
    Demands my soul, my life, my all!'

Isaac Watts
1674–1748

JULY

20

21

In 1969, American astronaut Neil Armstrong took the first steps on the moon.

22

Born 1844, W.A. Spooner, Oxford clergyman, renowned for such verbal slips as 'half-warmed fish' when he meant 'half-formed wish'.

23

24

JULY

25

The feast day of James, brother of John, fisherman and follower of Jesus, the first of the apostles to be martyred.

26

Died 1881, George Borrow, English writer and linguist who translated the Bible into Manchu Chinese.

27

George Borrow
1803–81

George Borrow, the author of *Lavengro* and *Romany Rye*, was a talented linguist. He was able to converse not only in Latin, French, German, Danish, Welsh and Gaelic, but also in Romany, the language of the gypsies. He wrote his two best-known books after spending seven years among the travelling people and went on to use his gift to translate the Bible into a number of languages, including Chinese, while working for the British and Foreign Bible Society.

JULY

28

Died 1750, Johann Sebastian Bach, German organist and composer of cantatas, oratorios, masses and pieces for organ, clavier, violin and cello, perhaps best known for his orchestral work 'The Brandenburg Concertos'.

29

30

31

The feast day of Ignatius Loyola, born in 1491, who was a Spanish soldier and founder of the Jesuit movement, which was involved in education, foreign missions and social service.

Desert
by H. Armstrong Roberts

AUGUST

Morning Glory

---

(1)

---

(2)

---

(3)

AUGUST

4

5

6

*Born 1809, Alfred Lord Tennyson, English poet whose works included
such classics as 'In Memoriam' and 'The Lady of Shalott'.*

7

8

*Died 1471, Thomas à Kempis, German Augustinian monk, writer, preacher,
counsellor and author of 'The Imitation of Christ'.*

AUGUST

9

10

*Died 258, Lawrence of Rome, who when asked by his persecutors
to produce the treasures of the church, brought out the poor.*

11

*Died 1778, Augustus Toplady, clergyman and hymnwriter, author of
'Rock of ages, cleft for me'.*

'*It is good for us to encounter troubles and adversities from time
to time, for trouble often compels a man to search his own heart.
It reminds him that he is an exile here, and that he can put his
trust in nothing in this world. It is good, too, that we sometimes
suffer opposition, and that men think ill of us and misjudge us,
even when we do and mean well. Such things are an aid to
humility, and preserve us from pride and vainglory. For we
more readily turn to God as our inward witness, when men
despise us and think no good of us.*'

Thomas à Kempis
1379–1471

AUGUST

12

Died 1827, William Blake, painter, engraver, poet and mystic.

13

Died 1912, Octavia Hill, English housing reformer and one of the founders of the National Trust.

14

15

16

AUGUST

17

Born 1761, William Carey, the shoemaker-turned-missionary who became one of the pioneers of the modern missionary movement.

18

19

Died 1662, Blaise Pascal, French philosopher, mathematician and physicist, who wrote an unfinished apologia for the Christian faith, 'Pensées'.

'The God of Abraham, the God of Isaac, the God of Jacob, the God of Christians is a God of love and comfort, a God who fills the soul and heart of those whom he possesses, a God who makes them conscious of their inward wretchedness, and his infinite mercy; who unites himself to their inmost soul, who fills it with humility and joy, with confidence and love, who renders them incapable of any other end than himself.'

Blaise Pascal
1623–62

AUGUST

20

The feast day of Bernard of Clairvaux who died in 1153, abbot, theologian and founder of the Cistercian Order, who used the Bible extensively 'not so much in order to expound the words as to reach people's hearts'.

21

Born 1849, George Grenfell, missionary and explorer who charted the Congo.

22

23

24

Born 1759, William Wilberforce, English politician, philanthropist and campaigner against the slave trade.

AUGUST

---(25)---

Born 1799, John Dunmore Lang, Australian clergyman, politician and educationalist.

---(26)---

---(27)---

Born 1910, Mother Teresa, Yugoslavian nun who won the Nobel peace prize in 1979 for her work among the poor of Calcutta.

'*We need to find God, and he cannot be found in noise and restlessness. God is the friend of silence. See how nature – trees, flowers, grass – grow in silence; see the stars, the moon and sun, how they move in silence. Is not our mission to give God to the poor in the slums? Not a dead God, but a living, loving God. The more we receive in silent prayer, the more we can give in our active life.*'

Mother Teresa
Born 1910

AUGUST

28

Born 1828, Leo Tolstoy, Russian novelist, philosopher and Christian thinker.

29

30

31

*The feast day of Aidan, the Irish bishop who organized a monastery
to train missionaries on the island of Lindisfarne, and died in 651.*

Special events this month

SEPTEMBER

Rose

1

2

*Died 1973, J.R.R. Tolkien, English philologist and author of
'Lord of the Rings'.*

3

SEPTEMBER

4

5

6

In 1620, the Pilgrim Fathers set sail from Plymouth in 'The Mayflower'
to find religious freedom.

7

Born 1917, Leonard Cheshire, pilot and philanthropist,
who spent his post-war career helping the sick and disadvantaged.

8

SEPTEMBER

9

The ordination took place in 1912 of William Whiting Borden, a young millionaire who left his fortune to become a missionary.

10

11

Died 1531, Ulrich Zwingli, leader of the Protestant Reformation who proposed a more radical reform of the communion service than the other reformers.

'*A true saint is like a stream from a living spring which, though it may be greatly increased by a shower of rain and diminished in time of drought, yet constantly runs; or like a tree planted by such a stream, that has a supply at the root and is always green, even in time of the greatest drought.*'

Jonathan Edwards
Leading American theologian and philosopher
1703–58

SEPTEMBER

12

13

14

15

16

*Born 1906, J.B. Phillips, English clergyman who translated
the New Testament into modern English.*

SEPTEMBER

17

18

*Died 1905, George MacDonald, the Scots minister who wrote
the fantasy novels which influenced C.S. Lewis, J.R.R. Tolkien and others.*

19

*Born 1839, George Cadbury, Quaker, chocolate manufacturer
and social reformer.*

'O Light Invisible, we praise Thee!
Too bright for mortal vision.
O Greater Light, we praise Thee for the less
The eastern light our spires touch at morning,
The light that slants upon our western doors at evening,
The twilight over stagnant pools at batflight,
Moon light and star light, owl and moth light,
Glow-worm glowlight on a grassblade.
O Light Invisible, we worship Thee!'

T.S. Eliot
1888–1965

SEPTEMBER

20

Born 1888, T.S. Eliot, poet, dramatist and critic, born in the USA, who won the Nobel prize for literature in 1948.

21

22

Born 1791, Michael Faraday, physicist and chemist famous for his work in electro-magnetic induction.

23

Died 1879, Francis Kilvert, English curate whose 'Diary' is recognized as an important social document of the period.

24

Born 1759, Charles Simeon, Cambridge clergyman, preacher and writer, who inspired generations of students to Christian discipleship.

SEPTEMBER

25

26

27

*Born 1805, George Müller, German-born preacher and pastor
who founded an orphanage in Bristol, England,
relying solely on prayer and faith, without appeals for funds.*

*'The more I study nature,
the more I am amazed at the Creator.'*

Louis Pasteur
1822–95

SEPTEMBER

28

*Died 1895, Louis Pasteur, French chemist and bacteriologist who pioneered
the practice of immunization and the sterilization of milk.*

29

*In 1955, David Sheppard, English cricketer, was ordained
into the Church of England ministry.*

30

Coastline
by Martin Thonig

OCTOBER

Carnations

1

Born 1817, Benjamin Jowett, classical scholar and translator of the works of Plato, Anglican priest, and one of the great minds of the nineteenth century.

2

Born 1904, Graham Greene, novelist and author of 'The Power and the Glory'.

3

Died 1226, Francis of Assisi, Italian monk and founder of the Franciscan order of friars.

OCTOBER

4

Died 1582, Teresa of Avila, Spanish nun, religious reformer, and mystic.

5

6

*Burnt at the stake in 1536, William Tyndale, English Protestant leader
and Bible translator.*

7

*Born 1931, Desmond Tutu, South African bishop outspoken in his defence
of the oppressed.*

8

*Born 1882, Harold Moody, Jamaican-born doctor and leading light
in the Congregationalist movement.*

OCTOBER

9

Died 1940, Wilfred Grenfell, author and medical missionary in Labrador.

10

11

'Praised be my Lord God for all his creatures,
 especially for our brother the sun,
 who brings us the day and who brings us the light;
 fair is he and shines with a very great splendour;
 O Lord, he signifies you to us!'

Francis of Assisi
1181–1266

OCTOBER

12

*In 1913, wartime nurse Edith Cavell was executed
for helping soldiers to escape from occupied Belgium.*

13

*Died 1605, Theodore Beza, theologian, author, translator of the Bible
and assistant to John Calvin.*

14

*Born 1940 in India, Harry Webb, pop singer with a special concern
for the rights of the poor, better known as Cliff Richard.*

15

16

*Died 1555, Hugh Latimer, English Protestant reformer who was martyred
with Nicholas Ridley.*

OCTOBER

17

18

19

Died 1609, Jacobus Arminius, the Dutch theologian whose ideas influenced the evangelical revival of John Wesley and his followers.

'*Be of good comfort Master Ridley, and play the man. We shall this day light such a candle, by God's grace in England, as I trust shall never be put out.*'

Hugh Latimer
1485–1555

OCTOBER

20

21

22

23

24

OCTOBER

25

*Died 1820, John Bacon, American clergyman, legislator and judge
who worked for the rights of Negroes and Indians.*

26

Born 1911, Mahalia Jackson, one of the greatest of all American gospel singers.

27

*Born 1854, William Smith, Scots founder
of the Boys' Brigade movement in 1883.*

'Behold, Lord, an empty vessel that needs to be filled. My Lord,
fill it. I am weak in the faith; strengthen me. I am cold in love;
warm me and make me fervent, that my love may go out to my
neighbour. I do not have a strong and firm faith; at times I doubt
and am unable to trust you altogether. O Lord, help me.
Strengthen my faith and trust in you. In you I have sealed the
treasure of all I have. I am poor; you are rich and came to be
merciful to the poor. I am a sinner; you are upright. With me,
there is an abundance of sin; in you is the fulness of
righteousness. Therefore I will remain with you, of whom I can
receive, but to whom I may not give.'

Martin Luther
1483–1546

OCTOBER

28

29

30

Born 1821, Fyodor Dostoevsky, Russian writer whose novels explore the problem of suffering.

31

In 1521, Martin Luther, the German religious reformer, nailed his ninety-five theses to the church door at Wittenberg.

Changing colours
by H. Armstrong Roberts

Special events this month

NOVEMBER

Convolvulus

1

2

In 1953, Chad Varah, London clergyman, founded the Samaritans,
a service to befriend the suicidal and despairing.

3

NOVEMBER

4

*Born 1771, James Montgomery, Scots poet and hymnwriter,
author of 'For ever with the Lord'.*

5

6

*Died 1905, George Williams, English social reformer and, in 1844,
founder of the YMCA.*

7

*Born 1918, Billy Graham, the American evangelist who has preached
to more people than any other man in history.*

8

Died 1674, John Milton, poet best known for his epic poem 'Paradise Lost'.

NOVEMBER

9

10

11

> ' What in me is dark
> Illumine, what is low raise and support;
> That to the height of this great argument
> I may assert eternal Providence,
> And justify the ways of God to men.'

John Milton
1573–1631

NOVEMBER

12

Born 1615, Richard Baxter, English nonconformist preacher who wrote some 160 books on social, ethical and doctrinal issues.

13

Born 354, Augustine, Bishop of Hippo, who, after a wayward youth, became a leader of the church and one of its greatest thinkers.

14

Born 1797, Charles Lyell, Scots geologist, friend of Darwin and author of the influential 'Principles of Geology'.

15

16

Born 1811, John Bright, English politician, Quaker and campaigner for the rights of the poor.

NOVEMBER

17

18

*In 1651, Paul Gerhardt, German hymnwriter, was ordained
into the Lutheran church.*

19

'*You (O God) move us to delight in praising
you – for you have made us for yourself and
our hearts are restless till they find their rest in
you.*'

Augustine of Hippo
354–430

NOVEMBER

20

21

22

Died 1963, C.S. Lewis, Professor of Medieval and Renaissance Literature, Christian apologist and writer much loved for his children's stories about the land of Narnia.

23

Died 1585, Thomas Tallis, musician, organist and father of cathedral music.

24

Died 1572, John Knox, Scots theologian, historian and reformer of the church in Scotland.

NOVEMBER

25

Born 1880, John Flynn, founder of the Australian Inland Mission and one of the founders of the Flying Doctor Service.

26

27

'God made us: invented us as a man invents an engine. A car is made to run on petrol, and it would not run properly on anything else. Now God designed the human machine to run on Himself. He Himself is the fuel our spirits were designed to burn, or the food our spirits were designed to feed on. There is no other. That is why it is just no good asking God to make us happy in our own way without bothering about religion. God cannot give us a happiness and peace apart from Himself, because it is not there. There is no such thing.'

C.S. Lewis
1898–1963

NOVEMBER

28

Born 1628, John Bunyan, self-educated tinker, preacher and author of 'The Pilgrim's Progress'.

29

Born 1627, John Ray, botanist and naturalist who, with Carolus Linnaeus, founded modern scientific biology.

30

Snow-capped peaks
by Freidmar Damm

Special events this month

DECEMBER

Clematis

1

Executed 1581, Edmund Campion, first English Jesuit martyr.

2

*Hanged 1859, John Brown, American campaigner against slavery,
executed after leading an unsuccessful rebellion of slaves
at Harper's Ferry, Virginia.*

3

DECEMBER

4

5

Born 1830, Christina Rossetti, British poet and sister of poet and painter, Dante Gabriel Rossetti.

6

7

8

Died 1649, Martin Rinkart, German clergyman, poet, hymnwriter and musician, author of the hymn 'Now thank we all our God'.

DECEMBER

9

10

*Born 1822, César Franck, Belgian-born composer and organist,
known for his reflective organ works and his oratorio 'Les Béatitudes'.*

11

*Born 1918, Alexander Solzhenitsyn, exiled Soviet novelist and winner
of the 1970 Nobel prize for literature.*

'All that the downtrodden can do is go on
hoping. After every disappointment they must
find fresh reason for hope.'

Alexander Solzhenitsyn
Born 1918

DECEMBER

12

13

14

Born 1836, Frances Ridley Havergal, English hymnwriter, gifted singer and instrumentalist, author of the famous hymn of dedication 'Take my life'.

15

16

DECEMBER

17

*Died 1724, Thomas Guy, English philanthropist
and founder of Guy's Hospital.*

18

*Born 1707, Charles Wesley, prolific hymnwriter, leading light
of the early Methodist movement, and younger brother of John Wesley.*

19

*Born 1808, Horatius Bonar, Scots preacher and hymnwriter, author of
'I heard the voice of Jesus say, "Come unto me and rest"'*

*'Love divine, all loves excelling,
Joy of heaven, to earth come down!
Fix in us thy humble dwelling,
All thy faithful mercies crown:
Jesu, thou art all compassion,
Pure, unbounded love thou art;
Visit us with thy salvation,
Enter every trembling heart.'*

Charles Wesley
1707–88

DECEMBER

20

*Died 1552, Katherine Luther, German nun and, later,
wife of the famous reformer.*

21

*Died 1807, John Newton, converted slave dealer, preacher
and writer of many hymns, including 'Amazing Grace'.*

22

23

Born 1648, Robert Barclay, Scots Quaker and writer.

24

*In 1968, the Apollo 8 astronauts, Frank Borman, James Lovell
and William Anders, took it in turns to read verses from the opening chapter
of Genesis while orbiting the moon.*

DECEMBER

25

26

27

Born 1571, Johannes Kepler, German astronomer, famous for his work on planetary orbits.

> '*What can I give Him,*
> *Poor as I am?*
> *If I were a shepherd*
> *I would bring a lamb;*
> *If I were a wise man*
> *I would do my part –*
> *Yet what I can, I give Him,*
> *Give my heart.*'

Christina Rossetti
1830–94

DECEMBER

28

29

*Murdered in Canterbury Cathedral in 1170, Thomas à Becket,
English Archbishop and martyr.*

30

*Died 1892, Andrew Alexander Bonar, Scots pastor
who spent thirty-six years in a needy area of Glasgow.*

31

*Died 1384, John Wycliffe, one of the forerunners of the Protestant Reformation,
whose translation of the Latin Bible into English not only influenced
later translations but enabled people to read the scriptures for themselves.*

Woodland
by H. Armstrong Roberts

Copyright © 1987 Lion Publishing

Published by
Lion Publishing plc
Icknield Way, Tring, Herts, England
ISBN 0 7459 1222 2
Albatross Books Pty Ltd
PO Box 320, Sutherland, NSW 2232, Australia
ISBN 0 86760 867 6

First edition 1987

Compiled by Jon Reynolds

Quotations from copyright material are as follows: *Mere Christianity*,
C. S. Lewis, Fount Paperbacks; *Something Beautiful for God*, Malcolm
Muggeridge, Fontana; *Collected Poems 1909–62*, T. S. Eliot, Faber and
Faber Ltd, UK/Harcourt Brace Jovanovich, USA; *Edges of His Ways*,
Amy Carmichael, SPCK, UK/Christian Literature Crusade, Washington
PA, USA

Photographs by ZEFA UK, except 'June' by Sonia Halliday Photographs:
Sonia Halliday and 'August' by Cephas Picture Library: Mick Rock

Cover and text illustrations by Chris Barker

Printed and bound in Spain